DEDICATION

The Author dedicates this volume to his Grandchildren of the New Millennium Ellen Sarah and James Angus, and for all children of our 21st Century. This book is published in the hope that they will grow up to love and honour their family traditions and folklore. Hopefully they will not feel the past is another country inhabited by ancestors of another world.

The Illustrator Ruth Bayley dedicates her Artwork to the memory of her parents.

Alpine Legends

of Switzerland

A TREASURY OF STORIES
MYTHS AND
MOUNTAIN MYSTERIES

RE-TOLD BY
MARK STEINER

ILLUSTRATED BY
RUTH BAYLEY

Alpine Legends

This edition published in 2005
by Nevis International Books, Atlantic House, Island of Seil, near Oban, Argyll PA34 4RF

Designed by Ruth Bayley.

A catalogue record of this book is available from the British Library.

ISBN 0-9550-778-2-6

Printed in Scotland by www.nevisprint.co.uk

ACKNOWLEDGEMENTS

The Author appreciates the encouragement of a true daughter of Switzerland, Hanni Muff-Arnold of Luzern, a Lady of Letters. Her tenacious care and concerns for Swiss culture and heritage and her devotion to Switzerland's languages and literature has instilled her own gentle charm and joyful felicity to her own cherished Swiss folklore.

Special appreciation also to Lilly Trindler of Bern for her internationally recognised professional support as a stalwart of the Schweiz Kurzwellendienst of the Swiss Broadcasting Corporation and the English Club of Bern. Her mastery of English and her teaching skills have inspired three generations of pupils in Switzerland and the English-speaking world.

The Author alone is answerable for any faux pas for which he may be justly chided.

CONTENTS

FOREWORD

by
Dr Eleanor M. Steiner of Fribourg

Switzerland is a beautiful land of snow-capped mountains, blue lakes, flower-carpeted alpine meadows, quaint villages and picturesque old wooden chalets.

It is also a dramatic land steeped in magic and mystery with a rich tradition of spell binding fireside folktales and romantic fables. It is a Homeland of heroes, like the fearless William Tell, who was born free, who lived free and who died free. There were also wicked villains whose mountain castles still overlook the lush green valleys.

It is also the Homeland of the fiercely independent, freedom loving mountain families whose struggles against winter snowstorms, avalanches and harsh daily toil make them a proud, hardy people.

The Alpine adventures and mountain mysteries are as interesting and entertaining as each mountain, lake, village and valley with its own legend.

The stories are as varied as the Swiss people themselves, Protestants, Catholics, Humanists, all with their various languages: French, German, Italian and Romansch and who all live peaceably together under their Alpine Motto "All for One, and One for All."

This Treasury of gripping tales of Switzerland is told by Grandfather Mark in his family's old wooden chalet, high in the Alps, overlooking the quaint little village and the blue lake down in the green valley in the heart of his beloved Homeland.

He tells his own folktales in his own way on cold winter nights, or warm summer evenings to the family of Grandmother Lilly, Grandson Rudie, Granddaughter Ellen, not forgetting Hunter the sheepdog, Milky the cat and Springer the kid goat –while Father is in the cattle shed milking the cows.

This treasury of Grandfather's timeless Alpine legends, homely fireside fables, gripping mountain mysteries and romantic myths has passed down in the family by word of mouth, in the Swiss oral tradition, from generation to generation as *"Tales my Grandfather told me."* This is part of a family heritage just as much as the family's old Grandfather clock and Grandma's ancient spinning wheel.

Grandfather's traditional folklore and tales are inspired by the dramatic landscape and remarkable Swiss people. Most of the characters, although life-like, are actually fictitious in folk tale tradition.

Just as generations of children and their parents have loved and enjoyed Johanna Spyri's classic Heidi adventures in the land of legends, now, with these stories, children and their parents—can enjoy and love Grandpa Mark's own re-told Tales and Aunt Ruth's enchanting illustrations.

Tales My Grandfather Told Me

THE TALE OF WILLIAM TELL
THE SWISS NATIONAL HERO

EVERY country has its National Hero - for the Americans it is George Washington, England has Robin Hood, Scotland has Robert the Bruce, Australia has Ned Kelly and Switzerland has William Tell.

Our Swiss hero is William Tell. He was an ordinary man of the mountains who lived a simple life but whose extraordinary bravery made him respected among men and he became a symbol of courage and freedom for all peoples around the world.

He taught us how to tame a bully and not be frightened to speak up for ourselves. Our William Tell lived here in the heart of Switzerland long ago when our little country was ruled by foreign soldiers. We were not free men then.

So seven hundred years ago our menfolk of the valleys and

mountains near Lake Luzern the herdsmen, woodsmen and mountain men left their Alpine pastures, their cows and goats and their families in their cosy chalets. These men gathered together in a remote forest clearing. They would not live in fear of bullies and they decided to stand up to the cruel foreign soldiers and agreed to drive them from our Homeland.

That was how our free nation of Switzerland was born. By ordinary men who made a vow, who swore an oath with raised arms, and promised to stand together. "All for One and One for All" which is our own motto.

Those Founding Fathers of Switzerland were inspired by one man - The Bravest Fighter for Freedom - William Tell.

William was a Man of the Mountains, he was a chamois hunter. He followed those wild goat-like Alpine antelopes which are hard to see and even harder to capture. These shadowy, ghostly animals dwell in the mountains and bound silently across the fresh snow and icy rocks and disappear in the gloomy winter mists or in the summer haze that conceal the white Alpine peaks.

In the still early morning, William Tell would awaken in his old wooden chalet home to the tinkling of cowbells on the Alpine meadows. At dawn, he trudged in the fresh snow, sparkling in the sunrise, up the mountains to rescue injured cows or goats and to hunt for chamois or foxes and wolves that raided the farmers' chickens or lambs.

Over the shoulder of his rough leather jerkin was slung his food pouch with homemade bread, a wedge of cheese made by Tell's wife, Frau Hedwig, from their goatsmilk, and a handful of sweet walnuts. When he was thirsty he cupped his hands in an icy mountain stream and drank the water of melting snow.

In his strong leathery brown hand he carried his crossbow. His flowing grey hair and grey beard turned white when covered with the winter snowflakes.

Sometimes William would take his ten year old son Walter with him up the icy crags and snowfields. The lad soon learned to trust his father and follow the leaping chamois and hunt the eagles and hawks that swooped down on the lambs and kid goats.

Often down in the village of Aldorf, Walter would daydream of the mountain crags towering above the village. But his mother would sternly rouse him and declare "Walter, pay attention to what is here on earth instead of dreaming that you are up in the clouds."

Walter wanted to learn his lessons but he wanted even more to be a hunter, a marksman like his father who was the best archer in the valley. Hunter Tell's family depended for their livelihood on what William could sell in the village market. In times of harsh winters and avalanches the old folk of the village often relied on their hunter to provide venison or take Frau Hedwig's homemade bread to the market.

When William Tell was a boy, a wise old travelling scholar taught him that "The greatest wisdom is kindness" and that "Courage is the measure of a man." And that is what made William Tell the man he was, fearless, kind and courageous.

William and the foreign soldiers rarely met. They did not like to go up into the mountains, above the snowfields and glaciers to the icy peaks and William rarely visited the village, except on market days.

Now one day while William was rescuing an injured goat on the mountain, down in the village, the Austrian Governor of the District, a Tyrant called Gessler marched in with his foreign soldiers. There the Governor ordered his guards to chop down a graceful fir tree and to cut it into a pole to stand in the village square. Then Gessler ordered a soldier to place the Tyrant's feathered hat atop the pole.

Next Governor Gessler ordered his men at arms to draw their swords and force the villagers who passed the pole to kneel down before his feathered hat in obedience to the cruel Tyrant himself.

Naturally, our proud men folk of the local districts, the Cantons of Uri, Schwyz and Unterwalden resented the foreign Governor's insulting order.

So the Elders of the three districts sent messengers to the villages for the menfolk to gather on a lonely pasture by a forest above Lake

3

Luzern. This pasture called "The Rutli" is still here today. It is our national place of honour, with a flagstaff with our distinctive blood red flag with the snow white cross of Switzerland. It is the birthplace of our pride and cradle of our nation.

At "The Rutli" our forefathers vowed to free our land from the foreign Tyrant and his soldiers by storming the Governor's castle. But they needed a leader. A man of our people who cared and believed "All for One and One for All."

Our William Tell, the Alpine Hunter, the quiet Man of the Mountains was not at that Rutli meeting. He was aloft in the Alpine peaks hunting for food for his family and his neighbour, the white haired old widow Frau Agatha Brunner who lived alone in her tumbledown chalet with an empty larder and an old goat for milk and beehive for honey.

Our Mountain men have lonely, arduous lives hunting or rescuing injured animals to earn a living and doing with life what living is for. William was so high up that he never received the message of the Rutli gathering.

But the next day, William came down from the Alps to visit the Village with his son, Walter.

He was a fine figure of a man who walked with his head held high so he looked taller than his height and with his crossbow over his shoulder.

Son Walter proudly held his father's hand as they walked through the bustling Market Square with its noisy cows, bleating goats, squawking hens and ducks on sale and the old ladies in black dresses and white bonnets selling golden butter, aromatic cheeses, cherry pies and soft honey cake.

The old, white-haired widow Frau Agatha Brunner was selling her little clay pots of honey and she waved her bent old fingers in greeting to Hunter Tell and Walter who walked towards her to return her greeting. William and Walter strode past the pole topped with the Tyrant's feathered cap.

Immediately the Tyrant's soldiers drew their swords and set upon the Father and Son. The soldiers shouted and roared orders to William and Walter to bow down before the Governor's hat.

But William, who was strong enough to carry an injured animal over his broad shoulders down the mountains, shrugged the soldiers off his broad shoulders. Then with each strong hand he lifted the two soldiers holding Walter and swept them aside with his powerful arms, so their swords clattered over the cobblestones.

Then holding his head high, William looked straight into the eye of the giant soldier guarding the capped pole and said in a firm voice that echoed around the Market Place "I am William Tell. I was born free, I live free and I shall die free."

The giant soldier lifted his great sword and all the other guards surrounded William and Walter. The giant then ordered William and Walter to kneel down before the pole with the Governor's hat.

William remained still; he did not flinch or tremble. The boy tightly clutched his Father's hand. Then Tell spoke with a strong voice that echoed around his beloved mountains above the village.

"Hear me, soldiers. I kneel only before God. I do not kneel before any King or Governor, or his foolish hat. I am a free man, not a slave."

The villagers all cheered and clapped in admiration of their hero's honesty and courage, but suddenly they fell silent as a troop of more soldiers marched into the village square.

Leading them was Governor Gessler with his thick black beard, and black bushy eyebrows, wearing his black cape and sitting astride his great black horse called Thunder. Then the Tyrant bellowed "William Tell, you have disobeyed my order. If you do not kneel before me and my hat I shall lock you up in my prison dungeon."

William Tell showed no fear. Instead he stroked the black horse's neck which calmed the great stallion. But Walter was fearful of the Tyrant with all the armed soldiers, so he clutched his father's hand even tighter.

Again William spoke in the same strong voice; "I tell you, Tyrant - I am a free man and we free men of the Mountains kneel down only before God - we will never kneel down to you or your empty hat."

The Governor had never before met such a fearless, honest man of courage.

The village hushed, even the noisy cockerel and the pigs and goats fell silent. The villagers continued to watch fearfully at the Man and Boy surrounded by armed soldiers. But the Tyrant looked even more furious; he bared his yellow teeth and shook his fist at William.

"William Tell, I shall show you and all these peasants what happens to anyone who defies me and my soldiers. I shall punish you with your own crossbow."

With that Governor Gessler pulled on the reins of his black stallion and Thunder reared up on his hind legs high above young Walter. Gessler then ordered his soldiers to seize the boy and tie him blindfolded to the pole. The boy refused to be tied up or blindfolded, saying he would only stay still if he remained free like a free man. The Tyrant commanded his guard to take an apple from a market stall and place the apple on the boy's head.

"Now, William Tell I will let you use your crossbow one last time. You must shoot the apple off your son's head. If you hit the apple you and your son will live. If you miss and don't kill your son, then you and your boy will be kept as prisoners in my dungeon."

Father Tell put his crossbow to his shoulder. The silent villagers leaned forward - Old Frau Brunner prayed for their safety and the farmer covered his cockerel's cage with his cloak to silence the rooster. The children put their hands over their eyes, and the old men took off their hats to honour Walter's bravery. Walter's friend Marie began weeping.

The lad stood tied to the pole 80 paces from his father. William Tell took two arrow bolts from his quiver. He put one of the bolts in his belt and the other to the crossbow.

William slowly raised the bow and carefully took aim. He pointed the arrow at the green apple on the boy's golden hair. He felt pride in his steady, valiant son who did not flinch or quiver a lip.

With his eye fixed on the apple, his hand as steady as a rock, William released the bolt and - whoosh - the arrow bolt flashed in the sun like a lightning flash and - zing - it sliced the apple clean in half with two pieces falling at Walter's feet.

The villagers cheered a mighty roar of praise for their archer hero and the brave Walter. They all surged forward through the wall of soldiers while William untied his son and held him high on his shoulders.

The villagers cheered louder, the bell ringer rang the church bells, the rooster crowed, the goats bleated, the pigs grunted, the blacksmith clattered his hammer on the forge and Arni, the impish schoolboy stole an egg from the nearest poultry stall. Arni then threw the egg at the Tyrant's feathered cap on the pole and stained it like a yellow omelette. Marie clapped her hands and the old widow gave a pot of honey to the village beggar who was laughing at the Tyrant. Everyone was happy except Governor Gessler and his soldiers.

When all the noise and cheering stopped, the Tyrant leaned down from his stallion, Thunder, and growled to William and Walter "William Tell, that was a master shot. But why did you put the second arrow in your belt?"

William Tell with Walter still on his shoulders strode towards Gessler.

"I will tell you, Tyrant." replied William "If I had missed the apple and struck my son, my next target would have been your heart. And I would not have missed your heart."

The soldiers drew back and the Governor was alarmed by William's fearlessness. Walter could see the Tyrant was now trembling with fear. Like any bully, the Tyrant was more frightened of his victim when the victim is not frightened and shows no fear of the bully.

Still trembling, Gessler ordered his soldiers and guards to seize Tell and imprison him in the castle dungeon in the fortress across the Lake Luzern.

The troop of soldiers overpowered William and bound him in heavy iron chains. They dragged him to the lakeside and bundled him into the Governor's boat, which was manned by twenty oarsmen.

Gessler was triumphant and showed his yellow teeth when he

shouted at his prisoner. He was sure that Tell could not harm him now he was lying in chains in the bottom of the boat at the feet of the guards.

At the water's edge the villagers were downcast and stood together in silence as the oarsmen began to row along the lake which was darkening from blue to grey under gathering storm clouds.

The villagers scrambled back from the shoreline when the rumble of thunder and blasts of icy wind howled down from the snow-peaks where the Spirit of the Alps was angered by Gessler's injustice and tyranny.

All the folk hurried to the village church to pray for the safety of their hero on the storm beaten waters. The old widow gripped Walter's hand in her work-worn bent fingers as she whispered to him "Be not afraid for your father - his courage has always saved him and us - Courage has its own reward. Inside every bully is a frightened coward." Marie also held Walter's other hand and hoped that Widow Brunner was right because Marie was still scared.

While the villagers were safe within the thick stone walls of the church, outside the winds blasted down the mountain ravines. On the lake, tremendous waves sprayed white foam over the sides of the boat, splashing the oarsmen and Gessler.

On the shoreline, the lakeside fir trees were swaying in the gale and the fir cones were being rattled off the twisted branches into the swirling waters. The ducks had flown away from the wind tossed waves to the safety of the shore and the otters scrambled over the rocks for safety. The storm shutters over the windows of the church and the chalets in the valleys were clattering. The cows and goats in the pastures and Alpine meadows hurriedly trotted down to the farm barns to shelter. Up in the Alps, Frau Hedwig Tell bolted the rattling door of their old wooden chalet as she wondered and worried about why her husband and son were not home yet. Her worry grew as she waited in the kitchen with their supper of cheese and fresh toasted bread and steaming milk.

Out on the lake, it grew darker in the twilight gloom. The boat, with all its oarsmen and soldiers with William Tell in chains, was being dashed by the foaming waves nearer and nearer to the jagged rocks.

The helmsman shouted against the roar of the gale to Gessler that he was losing control of the tiller. Above the fury of the storm he again shouted to the Tyrant to free William Tell whose great strength would master the helm.

The Tyrant could bully frightened village folk but the Governor could not calm the storm and the Governor himself was now afraid of the raging waters. So the Tyrant ordered the soldiers to unchain and free William to help the helmsman control the boat. As soon as William was unbound he took the tiller, and he steadied the vessel to the relief of the anxious soldiers. Their respect for Tell the Mountain Man was now greater than their fear of the Tyrant.

With William, The Man of the Mountains in command of the boat's tiller and in command of the oarsman, he ordered them to row the boat into the safety of calmer waters. William steered the boat near to a small table-rock that he knew in the lake and which lay just below the waves.

As he steered closer to the submerged rock William suddenly jerked the tiller so the boat veered out again towards the open lake.

Just as suddenly William grabbed his crossbow and quiver and in one great leap he jumped out of the boat onto the rock, leaving the boat to be swept out to the middle of the lake by a great wave.

Our hero was safe, free of his captors and Gessler was again angrily shaking his fist at William, who stood proudly on the rock.

That night William swam ashore but he could not go back to his chalet for he was an outlaw, a man on the run from the Tyrant whose soldiers would soon be hunting William as he had hunted the chamois and wolves. So he stayed the night in a goatherd's hut and dried his wet clothes by the bright log fire.

The next day the goatherd told William that Gessler's boat had weathered the storm and the Tyrant had turned back to the village where he and his soldiers had stayed the night, forcing the villagers out of their homes and eating all their food as well as forcing the children to polish the soldiers' boots. The herdsman said Gessler and his soldiers were returning to their fortress over the mountain tracks instead of rowing the boat along the lake again.

Now, we all know that our hero knew all the tracks and passes through the mountains as well as we know our way around our gardens. He knew that the Tyrant and his soldiers must return to the fortress along a rocky track through a narrow gorge. So William clambered up the mountain and jumped across a stream just like the sure footed mountain goat, the chamois.

Soon the tramp of marching soldiers with their rattling swords filled the gorge and the black bearded Tyrant on his black horse appeared. William stood up and in a strong voice that rang out across the gorge he said: "Gessler! Stop making a fool of yourself. Stop trying to be important. Instead try to do something useful."

Gessler stopped in his tracks. He ordered his soldiers to chase and seize William. He offered a bar of gold to any soldier who killed William.

At 100 paces away from the Tyrant, William drew his crossbow and aimed at Gessler's heart. Then - whoosh - the arrow bolt zinged through the air straight at the Tyrant who was knocked off his horse and lay dead on the ground.

Without their Governor, the Austrian soldiers dropped their swords and fled down the mountain to their fortress and locked themselves inside with their own fear.

The news of the Tyrant's death echoed through the mountains as the herdsmen yodelled for joy and the Mountain men blew their Alphorns as a trumpet call for the people to fight for their freedom from cruel tyranny.

In the valleys and chalets the folk gave Thanksgiving. The village boys rang the church bells and in the meadows even the cows and goats romped about and clattered their cowbells. The Old Widow Brunner hugged Marie and said "I told you courage has its own reward. Inside every bully is a frightened coward."

That night the men folk gathered in the village squares throughout the districts and marched to Gessler's fortress where they drove out the foreign soldiers and set fire to the fortress.

That was the baptism of fire for the Swiss nation, the Confederation of Helvetia.

That is how William Tell, the Man of the Mountains, became the national hero of a freedom loving people.

And today in the village of Altdorf you can still see the spot where William Tell shot the apple off Walter's head!

THE ALPINE
TREASURE CAVE

WHEN Grandfather was a boy he lived in the remote village of Engelberg high up in the mountainous Canton of Unterwalden. And Grandfather's Grandfather told him this story of the mysterious Treasure Cave high up by the mountain pass.

Two young herdsmen were guarding their goats from the wolves that prowled among the lofty peaks and pine forests when a Stranger came striding down the mountainside and greeted them.

The newcomer was an outlandish figure with a soldierly bearing in a short tunic, a bright breast plate and a red cloak over his shoulder. He saluted the two Goatherds in a strange language, but when they shook hands not understanding, he spoke to them in the ancient Alpine language of Romansch.

He asked them to guide him to the Black Cave on the

mountainside. The young herdsmen were surprised that a Stranger should have heard of the secluded Black Cave. They were even more astonished that anyone would want to go to the mysterious forbidden cavern that generations of Engelbergers had fearfully shunned because of its dreaded reputation as the haunted tomb of a Roman Centurion.

The older Goatherd, Franz, who was a cautious, prudent mountain man, remained silent. But the younger, impetuous Goatherd, who was known as Hasty Hans, agreed to show the Stranger up to the Cavern - but only on one condition: under no circumstances must the Stranger utter a sound to disturb the silence of the haunted Cave. No matter what he saw or heard. The Stranger agreed he would not speak or disturb the centuries long peace of the deep silent Cave.

So Hans led the Stranger up the steep rock face to the mountainside waterfall which hid the Black Cave behind the cascading screen of the gushing Alpine Spring.

Hans explained they would be able to walk deep inside the Cavern, but there everything would be as black as night.

The Stranger nodded his understanding and as they both clambered up the rocky mountainside to the waterfall, the Stranger began muttering in a strange language like the Latin sung by the black monks in Engelberg's monastery far down in the valley. The Stranger did not look like a monk but more like a military man, a Soldier of long ago, as he marched to the Cave.

As they entered the dark cave both were silent and the only sound was the splashing waterfall at the entrance. When they ventured deeper down inside the Cavern over rocks and around a bend in the tunnel suddenly the whole Black Cave was lit up by a lightning blue flash.

In the glare they saw a skeleton on the floor in the middle of the cave with a Treasure Chest beside the bones.

Hans was overawed and terrified.

But the Stranger stood firm and erect with his right arm raised in salute to the skeleton. He then declared in a strong, clear voice "Salve" - a Latin greeting.

The Roman soldier's salutation shattered the silence and "Salve" echoed and thundered around the Cavern until it was drowned by the roar of rocks crashing around the Cave that was shaking and trembling like an earthquake.

As the rocks split open gleaming nuggets of gold cascaded down from the cave roof and the skeleton's Treasure Chest burst open and sparkling gemstones tumbled out.

The rumbling rockfall shook the mountain and the tremors reverberated across the Alps and along the valley.

Outside the Black Cave, Franz the Goatherd feared for his friend Hans. Franz scrambled up to the mountainside to the Cave to rescue Hans and the Stranger.

At the Cave entrance Franz found his young friend crawling from the dark cavern looking horror-stricken, dumbfounded and unable to speak. He was clutching a handful of gold nuggets and gemstones, but had lost his mind.

Franz ran down to the valley to get help for his young friend. While Franz was away, young Hans crawled to the waterfall and, still clutching the gold and gemstones, Hans threw himself off the rock into the deep water of the pool far below.

Neither Hans nor his handful of treasures were ever seen again. The Black Cave with the two Centurions was sealed tight with rocks by Franz and the villagers.

So, the secret of the mountain still remains a secret.

THE VILLAGE FOUNTAIN
A BULLY SAYS SORRY

THE village of Altbach is an ancient village of old wooden chalets with window boxes of red and white geraniums, the same colours as the Swiss flag.

The only street, the narrow cobbled Langstrasse, curves through the village and links the small stone church at one end with the village square near the bustling cattle market at the other end.

But there was a time when unlike most Alpine villages, Altbach did not have a traditional water fountain in the village square. Instead Altbach's water well was at the crossroads on the village outskirts by the cattle market.

This meant the local folk had to walk each morning all the way to the crossroads waterwell to fill their water pails even in the winter, when the snow was deep. And, in the summer, cowherds drove their cattle through Langstrasse past the village square to the market.

It was all very hard, especially in the winter when the cobblestones were icy, or in summer with the cattle in the Langstrasse, for the old women and children to haul their heavy water pails back home.

One frosty winter morning the poor village widow, Frau Hermine Huber, was carrying two heavy pails of water for her six children when she slipped on the icy cobbles and spilt all the water. The village Mayor, Herr Meier was walking past. The poor widow stopped him, and told the Mayor that if he wanted to be elected again he should listen to the villagers and organise a water fountain to be built in the village square.

All the villagers agreed with Widow Huber and they all, even the poorest peasants, collected pennies to pay Altbach's stonemason and blacksmith to build the village square water fountain - everyone, that is, except the valley's richest landowner and cattle-dealer, Farmer Haag. He was a miserly, selfish bully who was unpleasant to the villagers, and cruel to his animals. The rich landowner refused to give any money because he said he and his cattle did not need a water fountain as he had his own spring water.

The day the splendid new village fountain was officially opened by the Mayor and blessed by the Priest, everyone in the valley crowded into the village square for the ceremony, and to applaud Widow Hermine Huber when she released the water cascade!

Everyone came except Farmer Haag, who stayed at home counting his money.

The next day, the day after the splendid new fountain was officially opened, Farmer Haag and his cowherds drove his cattle down Langstrasse to the village cattle market.

When he reached the water fountain the big Black Bull, who was leading the herd saw the fountain cascading into the stone water trough. And being thirsty, the Black Bull stopped to gulp the drink, and the herd of cows stopped behind him.

Farmer Haag was angry at the delay and he beat the Black Bull with his stick. And, of course, this made the Bull furious, so furious that with a great bellow of anger, the huge beast gave a great heave, and pushed over the stone trough and the bright shiny brass water pipe. The villagers were aghast, and then horrified as the great Black Bull turned on Farmer Hagg and with his long sharp horn he gored his cruel master in the leg. The Farmer yelled with pain from his badly injured bleeding leg.

The villagers wrung their hands in despair at the great misfortune - all their money had been wasted now the splendid village fountain was demolished by the Black Bull.

The poor folk would not have the money to build another village Fountain. It was Farmer Haag's misfortune that he would lose his leg and never walk again.

But the good folk of Altbach were not spiteful, and did not rejoice at the cruel man's misfortune.

The Priest and the villagers carried the injured farmer into the Church and the Mayor called for Widow Huber. She was the village herbalist and was wise in the ways of healing. She sent her son Andres back to her home to collect the box of potions, herbal remedies, ointment and oils. Soon she stopped the dying Farmer from bleeding to death and silenced his pained groaning and moaning by easing his agony and giving him clear orders and prescriptions. No one had spoken to him like that before and although he did not like Frau Huber's bitter medicine, she did not allow him to argue with her medical orders, and he found that the more he did what he was told the quicker he got better.

Soon he was well and he left the Church and Frau Huber's care and he limped back to his house.

The next day he sent his servant to the village with a summons to the village Mayor, the Widow Huber and the Priest to come to attend him.

When Herr Meier, Widow Huber and the Priest arrived at the Landowner's splendid residence he greeted them in a most unusual friendly and neighbourly manner.

Farmer Haag apologised for the Black Bull's damage to the village fountain.

He thanked Widow Huber for her herbal skills in saving his life, and also saving his leg.

And, he thanked the Priest for taking him into the church and calling Frau Huber to nurse him.

Next he promised he and his herdsmen would not lead and drive his herds along Langstrasse and the village square to the cattle market anymore.

The Mayor, the poor Widow and the Priest were dumbfounded with surprise.

They were even more astonished when the miserly unneighbourly landowner gave them each a purse of gold coins. He told the Mayor to use the gold to build a splendid new waterfall and to call it "Frau Huber's Fountain". Then he told the poor Widow to buy a new chalet and more healing herbs, potions and ointments for her first aid box. And lastly he told the Priest to buy a new bell for the Church tower.

Today when you visit Altbach you can drink cool, crystal water cascading from Frau Huber's Fountain in the village square and listen to the new Church bell. And you won't be bothered by the herds of cows and goats trotting along Langstrasse.

THE SECRET
OF THE CASTLE

THERE are many ancient Castles in Switzerland, some are proud landmarks to a proud history, like Chateau Chillon, on Lake Geneva. Other ruined Castles stand like gloomy monuments to a gloomy past.

A few of the old Castles remain standing despite the harsh winds of time. They have become abandoned, or haunted and veiled in the mists of mystery.

Such an ancient, deserted Castle is the Chateau Finster, in the Overland.

Long ago, Castle Finster was the last stronghold of a rich aristocratic family, the Finsters and those Overlords ruled the valley, the villages and the alpine farming folk with high taxes, and punished the poor cowherds and goatherds, who could not pay their taxes or work for their masters.

The richer these wealthy Overlords grew, the more greedy and cruel they became.

Yet despite all their riches and hoard of treasure, their wives did not have any children, no descendants to carry on the name Finster and to go on living in the Castle. So, the proud old Chateau became empty and withered away like the old dead oak tree that still stands gaunt and leafless in the Castle grounds.

The haughty, overbearing family died out without leaving any children as heirs to their titles and their Castle. And, the cruel aristocrats were so greedy and grasping that, when they died they took their treasures to be buried with them in their graves.

When the last Overlord died, the Chateau was bolted and locked, so that the Castle would never again be used as a fortress to rule over the valley.

None of the villagers, or local mountain people, ever wanted to go to the forbidding Castle because they knew the ghosts of the dead Finsters haunted their family Chateau as punishment on their family for their cruelty. So the castle kept its dark secrets and treasures behind its bolted and locked great door.

Many, many years later two young men, strangers to the Alps, came to the valley. They were unpleasant and overbearing when they arrived in the valley tavern, and demanded beer and food. When they refused to pay for their meal and demanded overnight lodgings to sleep, the Innkeeper and the villagers did not offer their usual hospitality to the two villains. The two young bullies then threatened the village Mayor with their swords and demanded that he find them a hostel for the night. The old Mayor could not fight them, so he could only outwit the young villains, whose youth and inexperience were no match against the wily old man's cunning and learning in life.

The crafty Mayor had been elected by the villagers to protect them from outlaws and villains and he knew how to make fools of the bullies and teach them a lesson.

So, he gave them the key to the haunted Castle, that they might live like Lords in the Chateau.

Of course, the two arrogant strangers were proud of themselves for getting the keys to the Castle to live like Lords, and off the drunken pair staggered to sleep in the Castle that they did not know was haunted by the ghosts of the cruel Finsters.

The next day the two strangers were not seen in the village and did not return to the tavern.

The Mayor and his Councillors paraded up to the Castle. To their horror they found the two young strangers lying dead on the stone floor of the great Banquet Hall - the Bullies had been killed by their own swords.

The Mayor and his Councillors grabbed the Castle keys and hurried back to the village and tried to forget the mysterious murders.

Many years later another young stranger arrived at the village on a cold, wet night looking for lodgings. He was a poor student, and at the Tavern he only could afford a glass of milk and a slice of bread. He was a pleasant, courteous young man, Hans Peter, but the innkeeper explained there just wasn't anywhere for him to sleep overnight because it was Market Day and all the lodgings had been taken by the farmers.

The young student politely asked if he could stay the night in the big Castle. The Mayor and the Innkeeper were horrified, and advised the stranger not to go near the Chateau because it was haunted by the ghosts of the cruel and greedy Finsters.

The Mayor was concerned that the courteous Hans Peter should not come to harm in their pleasant village and they honestly told the young man what had happened to the two arrogant bullies in the Castle long ago.

Hans Peter listened politely and replied in a strong, clear voice that he had a clear conscience, he had done no one any harm so he had nothing to fear.

The modest, young man's honesty and courage were so obvious that the Mayor handed Hans Peter the keys to the Castle and insisted the young man take the Mayor's sword and the innkeeper's lantern to light the way just to be safe.

So Hans Peter went alone to the gloomy fortress of the long dead Finsters.

Inside the dark dungeons in the lantern light he found a cobweb covered bed, but he was so tired he fell onto the bed and was soon deeply asleep in the silent, black night.

At midnight Hans Peter was awakened by a loud banging and an ugly old dwarf carrying a shovel who told the young man to follow him. Hans Peter grabbed the lantern and sword and followed the dwarf down the stone steps to the cellar vault. In the flickering lantern light with ghostly shadows darkening the damp, musty walls, he could see the Finster's family vault with the aristocrats' names.

The dwarf then told the young man to dig a hole, and as Hans Peter dug deeper and deeper a stone coffin was unearthed. When he tried to move the lid a snake slid out of the coffin, hissing and coiling on the floor at the dwarf who shrank back with fear. But the young man was not afraid, and he swung his sword to cut off the snake's head.

Instantly the old dwarf changed into an old herdsman who had vanished from the valley long ago and had been imprisoned in the Castle because he couldn't pay his taxes.

The grateful herdsman thanked Hans Peter for freeing him from the curse of the Overlord and his imprisonment. He said if the young man had not helped him and had behaved badly like the two villains long ago, Hans Peter too would not have left the castle alive.

But now he told the young man to go back to sleep, and get a good night's rest.

The next morning when Hans Peter awakened he searched for the herdsman, and as he went down to the dungeon again, his footsteps echoed against the stone walls. He shivered as he passed along the dark cells with the black bats hanging heads down from the roofs until he reached the vault of the dead aristocrats.

When Hans Peter looked down into the grave he saw the nobles' skeletons with a treasure trove of gold coins and sparkling jewels that the Finster Overlords had stolen over the centuries from the villagers and valley folk.

Hans Peter was gazing thoughtfully at the misery the cruel Overlords had inflicted on the poor people but how the treasure did not give them peace in their tomb.

While he was standing there he heard the echoes of men shouting his name. Then the Mayor and his Councillors appeared before him. Breathlessly the Mayor said "Thank Goodness you are safe." And when the Mayor and his Councillors looked in the open tomb they stared in wonderment at all the gold coins and jewels among the skeletons.

Hans Peter looked at the poor villagers whose families had for generations been robbed and taxed by the Finster Overlords and he remembered the kindness of the Mayor and innkeeper to him when he had arrived as a friendless stranger in the friendly village and needed somewhere to sleep.

The young man smiled at them saying "All this treasure belongs to you. The nobles bought the treasures with taxes from your village. Take it all. I have no use for treasure. I am a Wayfarer - All I need is a meal and somewhere to sleep. Now I must be on my way."

Then picking up his small bundle of possessions, he walked out of the Chateau Finster into the sunny valley. Behind him the Castle still stands, and is now always ready to shelter him for the night if he ever returns again on a cold wet evening.

As Hans Peter strode down the valley with his head held high, on the Alpine pasture on the mountainside the Old Herdsman wished the young Wayfarer "Fare Well" in life.

BRAVING THE SNOWSTORM
ELSI, THE FEARLESS MILKMAID

LONG ago in our valley, the severe September frosts heralded a harsh winter when a carpet of snow covered the Alpine meadows and ice floated on the mountain streams.

As the autumn passed to winter, outside the cosy chalets with their log-fires, the cruel Old Man Winter ruled his white wrapped realm with fierce blizzards of more snow and icy winds.

Inside their snug homesteads, the Alpine farmers and herdsmen busied themselves carving wood or making butter and cheese, while their womenfolk baked fresh bread and honey cakes.

In his Chalet Sunnematt, meaning the Sunny Meadow House, Farmer Berger was about to make cheese when he discovered he had foolishly forgotfully left some of his dairy tools up in the Herdsmen's Alpine hut high up on the mountain pasture. Forgetful in his haste when the blizzard forced him to hurry down to the safety of his home and family.

Farmer Berger gathered his wife and children together and explained his problem - his predicament that he must recover his dairy tools from the Alpine hut.

He asked his sons Fritz and Franz if they would climb back up to the hut to collect his tools. The two lazy sons remained silent, not answering their father's request but still warming their hands by the log fire.

Fritz and Franz had heard from the village gossips that in the winter snowstorms, the Alps were haunted by mischievous phantoms and spiteful goblins. They played tricks on herdsmen and set off avalanches that swept snow and rocks down the mountainside. All the menfolk who herded cattle and goats on the high pastures and peaks knew the dangers of the alps outside and sought the comfort and safety of their ancestral chalet homes.

Mother Ruth was tearful and thoughtful. The likelihood that all of that cows' milk and goats' milk would go sour and be wasted meant the family would go hungry. But, she understood the young menfolk's fears and reluctance to risk their lives.

The whole family fell silent, downcast by all their misfortune and plight. The only sound was the fireside crackling and sparking of the pine logs and fir cones in the hearth.

Their daughter Elsi was quietly sitting in the fireside corner, bottle feeding a newborn weak kid goat. Slowly she stood up and passed the suckling kid goat and the milk bottle to Mother Ruth.

Elsi was a tall teenage girl with hair the colour of buttermilk and sky blue eyes. Her strong, sun bronzed arms were hardened by helping to make hay in the meadows, tending the animals and helping her father with churning milk into butter and cheese with the wooden milk paddle and dairy utensils.

Standing between her two brothers, she told Fritz and Franz in her quiet but firm voice "Father has worked hard milking our cows and goats and we will not let our milk go sour and be wasted."

Then Elsi spoke directly to her father "I will go up to our hut and fetch our dairy tools."

Farmer Berger shook his head disapprovingly saying "My beloved Elsi - it is too dangerous to defy the Spirits of the Mountain or avalanches."

Her brother joined in "Father is right. It is too scary."

Elsi stood tall, saying "Father, the Spirits may frighten men but why should they frighten me? They should not harm me. I have not harmed them." Then turning to Fritz and Franz, she said "Just because you are scared, you don't scare me. You were both scared when we were children. You said there were goblins under the bed until I looked and told you both you were being silly."

Then Elsi picked up her long red winter cloak, her rucksack, as well as her lantern and her climber's walking staff.

As Elsi stepped out into the cold darkness, she clutched her lantern tightly and trudged through the deep snow up the mountain track which was disappearing under the snowfall.

The harsh wind howled and the snowflakes quickly turned to ice on her face. Her red cloak also turned white with snowflakes and ice. As the wind swirled around her, the lantern's candle flickered. It was hard to see the hut, which lay under thick snow and was only recognised by the chimney still above the snow.

Elsi struggled on against the swirling icy snowstorm and managed to force open the hut door then wearily staggered inside.

In the weak light of the flickering candle Elsi saw the dairy tools and the milking stool and she sat down to rest.

In the loneliness of the old hut Elsi listened to the strange noises in the snowstorm outside and the wild winds battering against the little log cabin.

The faint candle light cast strange shadows on the walls when suddenly the lantern flickered and falteringly died out into the blackness of the wintry night.

The silence was only disturbed by outside storms. This was avalanche weather, when the snowfall and sheet ice would slice off the rock face and crash down the mountainside, driving and sweeping everything before it and scouring the fir forests and the log cabins down to the valley far below.

Elsi did fear the winter avalanches and the summer forest fires which also set the Mountain meadows, the log cabins and even the Chalets ablaze.

These are real dangers that all sensible mountain folk and alpine climbers or skiers respect as certain perils. It is wise to fear known dangers.

Amid the roar and rumblings outside in the storm, Elsi was aware of strange noises all around her outside the dark log cabin. She sat still and quiet on the milking stool, the mysterious ghostly sounds grew louder and louder....it was the weird wailing and howling of the mountain phantoms and the yells of the alpine goblins and forest dwarfs as they clambered down the chimney.

In the darkness Elsi could see nothing but she could smell the stink of the strange creatures as they shuffled towards her.

A ghostly voice in the chimney place shrieked "Catch her! Grab her!" and Elsi felt her cloak being pulled.

Another goblin replied "I can't catch her. I can't hold her. Her cloak is covered in snow and ice."

Elsi gripped her hiking staff and brandished the thick stick all around her in the darkness. A goblin yelled "She's hit me" and another creature shrieked "She's got a big stick - I'm getting out" and with that the goblins scrambled back up the chimney, trying to escape.

Elsi called out loudly after them "I am Sunnematt Berger's Elsi. I'm not frightened of you. You only scare people who think you are scary. But you don't scare me."

Then she picked up her rucksack with the dairy tools and left the cabin to trudge through the snow down to the Berger's chalet.

At home, the family rejoiced at her return and fussed over her as they took off her snowy cloak, her climbing boots and emptied the rucksack with all the precious dairy tools. After Mother sat Elsi in the warm fireside chair, the family listened in astonishment as she told them of her adventure and escapade.

Father Berger proudly put his arm on Elsi's shoulder and told Fritz and Franz "Some things are stronger than fear, like courage to face the fear."

The two brothers looked downcast, ashamed of their cowardice. Fritz mumbled "I would have come with you, if you had asked me." Franz added "I will come with you the next time."

Elsi just smiled and said nothing. But Father Berger declared "There won't be a next time. I won't leave the tools in the hut again."

Then he told the two brothers to go outside and chop up more logs for the winter fires.

And Mother Ruth was busy in the kitchen making a special breakfast of fresh bread with golden butter and honey and a hot chocolate drink for Elsi Berger, the fearless Heroine of the Alps.

THE HONEST MAN'S REWARD

IN the local tavern three village men were enjoying a glass of wine and fondue cheese. As the wine and the log fire warmed them, so their table talk became heated while they discussed their beliefs and faiths.

A travelling Philosopher, who was journeying along the alpine valley, stopped at the tavern for a rest. He was wandering through the mountain villages searching for an Honest Workman to reward.

The wise old Philosopher sat by the fireside corner listening to the three men, a Beggar, a Preacher and a Woodcutter discussing what is good and evil, what is right and wrong, real and unreal.

As the dispute became an argument, the Preacher banged the table with his fist and rebuked the Beggar and the Woodsman and advised them to heed his preaching. "After all" said the Preacher "I am nearest to the Lord."

This angered the Beggar, who retorted "No, you're not. I'm just as close to the Lord as you. After all, I don't need to work because the Lord still provides me with other people's food and wine." And with that the Beggar helped himself to another glass of the Preacher's wine and another helping of the Woodsman's fondue.

The Preacher was indignant and turned to the Woodcutter saying "Surely Woodsman you will agree I am nearest to the Lord."

The Woodsman was a quiet thoughtful man who toiled long and laboriously alone in the forest and preferred to listen and learn, rather than to talk and prattle. He shook his head slowly and took a deep breath. "All I know about such things" he said "Is that a man must do his work and leave the Lord to do his. I don't know who is nearest to God, but what I do know is that when I work hard I feel the Lord is near me, Then I listen to Him instead of talking at Him."

So there the threesome were without any agreement. The Preacher called over to the old Stranger in the fireside corner saying "You look like a wise man. Surely you agree that I am nearest to the Lord, don't you?" The wise old Philosopher stroked his white beard and paused before answering: "It's difficult to say. Rather than express a hasty, thoughtless opinion, I would prefer to judge you on your behaviour, not your boasting." Then he suggested the three men go home and sleep on the problem. In the morning they could each go off in different directions and do whatever they wanted to do. When they returned tomorrow night they could tell him what happened to each of them, and the wise old man could judge which of the three men were nearest to the Lord.

The threesome thought this was a good idea and on this at least they finally agreed.

At the end of the next day, the trio returned to the Tavern and the Philosopher.

"Well, men" the old man greeted them "What did you do today?"

The Beggar asked for a large glass of wine and after he gulped it down, he asked for another. "Phewww" gasped the Beggar "I've had a very hard day. It was so hot today that I had to find a shady place under the old chestnut tree. And when I did manage to get some sleep I dreamed I was being cooked like a roast chestnut. So if you don't mind, good Philosopher, I would like another glass of wine."

While the Beggar greedily gulped down the third glass of wine and wiped his brow with his coat sleeve, the Philosopher pronounced his judgement.

"You, Beggar" said the old man sternly "You are not in the Lord's favour. All you do is laze around, pretending you can't work, when you could work.

"Your dream of being roasted was a warning that you will burn in Hell if you don't work like an honest man."

The Preacher nodded agreement with the Philosopher's judgement of the Beggar saying "You are quite right, Philosopher - 'To work is to pray - Laborare est orare' and 'By the sweat of thy brow thou shalt earn thy bread - or your wine!"

The wise old man turned to the Preacher and told him "And you must not flatter me to deceive me with your false praise. Instead tell us what you did today."

The Preacher puffed himself up and pompously announced that he had endured a difficult day to test his goodness.

"I saw a strange, mysterious apple tree laden with large golden apples when all the other trees in the orchard were bare and fruitless.

So I picked a seemingly delicious apple. But when I took a bite I bit on a horrid maggot inside. Then I picked another seemingly good golden apple but when I bit into that one it was all brown and rotten inside.

"So I picked a third seemingly delicious apple and when I tried to eat it a wasp crawled out and stung my lip.

My lip was still stinging until I ate a fourth apple which did not seem so good, but was truly wholesome and healing."

The Preacher asked the Philosopher what his experience meant. The wise old man did not hesitate with his verdict and explained

"Preacher that is the Lord's judgement on you. Of all your seemingly good sermons only one in four, only a quarter, is truly wholesome and healing. Your sermons are humbug like your boast that you are nearest to the Lord."

The Preacher was left speechless for the first time any villager could remember.

The Philosopher then turned to the Woodcutter and asked him if he had been daydreaming like the Beggar, or gobbling bad fruit like the Preacher that day.

The Woodsman looked tired and weary while he hesitated and explained it had been just another hard day's work for him in the forest. Some old trees had been blown down in last winter's storm and he had to cut them into logs.

While he was chopping the logs the village widow, a little old lady called Frau Hanni wandered in the forest searching for mushrooms and collecting firewood to warm her little chalet on the mountainside.

The little old lady waved to the Woodcutter and offered him some of her few mushrooms but he declined her kindness as he knew she was poor and looked hungry. And when the Woodsman saw the old lady's small basket of firewood he said "That won't warm your chalet in the next snowstorm."

And with that he filled his large woodsman's sack with a load of special dry logs and hauled the heavy load over his shoulder to the old widow's mountainside chalet. The old lady was overjoyed but the wood cutter did not want to be thanked but marched back to the forest to fill his sack again with another heavy load of logs for Frau Hanni.

"And what happened next?" asked the Philosopher. The tired and weary Woodcutter again hesitated and then modestly explained "Well, winter is coming and the snow is falling so I went and loaded a third sack of logs for the old lady. That's why I would like to sit down and drink a large glass of milk."

The Preacher and the Beggar looked ashamed and they bowed their heads in embarrassment when the Philosopher told them: "Our Woodcutter is nearest to the Lord. He is one of the Lord's favourites because he works honestly, and he works for others. He is also wise because the greatest wisdom is kindness."

And with that the wise old man took a pouch of gold coins from his cloak and gave it to the Woodcutter as a reward. The Philosopher then travelled on to the next village.

The next day the old widow Frau Hanni carried a basket of fresh mushrooms to the Woodcutter's chalet as her gift to the modest, hardworking woodsman and his family. He paid her with a gold coin for the hungry old widow to buy food.

WHY DAISIES
BLUSH PINK...

ONE day Grandma and Grandpa took the family for a picnic on the floral meadow by the mountain stream.

Grandma laid down a linen cloth on the warm grass and spread out the picnic delicacies of newly baked home-made rye bread, golden butter, Emmentaler and Unterwaldner cheeses, honey cake, ripe black cherries and chocolate fingers with bowls of whipped cream. Mother opened the bottles of white and red grape juice.

While Grandpa and Jan went trout fishing in the stream, Ursuli and Grandma went picking posies of alpine flowers like the white Edelweiss and the blue Gentian, yellow Primroses, red Alpenroses, blue Soldanellas and little white Daisies. Grandma carefully plucked only one each of the flowers so that the Alpine cows, goats and sheep could also graze on the pasture blooms to make their creamy milk.

Grandma put a few little white Daisies with their pink petal tips in the middle of the picnic spread because the Daisy, or Margritli, as she called it, was her favourite flower. She then showed Ursuli how to make a Daisy chain garland.

While Grandpa sipped his wine he told the story of the Daisy. Long ago, when all Daisies were pure white and grew so thick they looked like snowfields even in hot mid-summer long after the snow had melted.

Grandpa told how on such a bright sunny summer day, the Daisies were gently swaying in the alpine breeze and fussily chattering among themselves. They were so absorbed in their prattle they did not notice a mountain traveller passing along the meadow.

The wayfarer was the Snow Queen of the Mountains who was strolling down from her Ice Palace on the frosty, lofty peak to enjoy the fragrance of the colourful alpine blossoms and to listen to the musical tinkling of the icicles at the Glacier stream.

As the Snow Queen passed by she stepped lightly in her ice crystal slippers to avoid treading on the flowers. The whole rainbow carpet of brightly coloured blooms, the herbs and blossoms in the mountain pasture all bowed their heads to the Snow Queen. The snow white Edelweiss, the striking blue Gentians and the bright yellow Primroses all respected the Mountain Code of Courtesy with the traditional Alpine greeting of "Grüss Gott", "God's Greeting", to the Snow Queen of the Mountains.

But the chattering, heedless Daisies failed to observe the Snow Queen until she had passed by on her return to her Ice Palace.

The daisies were so ashamed of their failure to honour the Code of Courtesy that they blushed with shame.

They blushed so much with embarrassment that their petals reddened with shame and tinged pink like blushing cheeks.

And that's why to this day the Edelweiss is still white, the Gentian is blue and the Primrose is yellow while Daisies' petals are like blushing cheeks.

THE GIRL WHO TALKED TOO MUCH

HIGH above the Alpine village on the lofty mountainside there is a dark cave which the old villagers say is an enchanted grotto, haunted by one of the Spirits of the mountains.

The village Elders and parents warn children not to climb so high up the rocky crags.

For generations no one, not even the grandfathers, the mountaineers or the goatherds had seen inside the dark, forbidden cave.

But there was one village girl, Gertrude who was very curious about the mystery of the grotto.

She was a dairymaid making cheese, butter and cream in the village dairy. Gertrude was a chatter box and often asked the old Dairyman,

Herr Keller about the cave. He would only shake his head and tell her to keep churning the milk like the other dairymaid, Elsa, a quiet, thoughtful girl.

Gertrude boasted to Elsa that she was not frightened of anyone or anything or even the Spirits of the Mountains.

Gertrude was a talker while Elsa was a listener who just nodded and continued making cheese and butter while Gertrude prattled on and on. It was even worse for Gertrude's brothers who had to listen to her at home every day. They called her Gertie, the Gabbler.

The more the boys ignored her the more Gertrude became determined to show everyone especially her modest brothers and the quiet Elsa, that she was cleverer and better than the others. She lay awake at night thinking of how she could be important and make everyone pay attention to her.

So on Sunday when the villagers were at church, Gertrude sneaked away and began climbing the mountainside to the forbidden cave.

It was a long climb over the rocky crags where the mountain goats scurried away from her and the Alpine Eagle, the Messenger of the Mountain Spirits swooped down as a warning to Gertrude to go back.

But the headstrong selfish girl recklessly climbed on and upwards, stopping only to pick wild mountain berries and look down at the little village. "I will show them I am better than they are." She said to herself and she continued upwards and upwards.

When Gertrude arrived at the cave she found a thorn bush covering the entrance and a snake guarding the passage to the grotto. She threw a stone at the snake who slithered away and she brushed aside the bush and ignored the thorns that scratched her hands.

As she entered the silent cavern a little old lady stood before her in the mysterious blue light of the cave. The lady had long silver hair and wore a long black cloak with a raven sitting on her shoulder.

"You are a foolish girl" she scolded Gertrude. "Go home before night falls and you get lost on the mountain."

But Gertie gabbled "I don't want to go down now. I want to go in the morning when the villagers will see me and I can show everyone I have been here."

The Old Lady saw Gertrude was a wilful and arrogant girl. If she wouldn't listen to advice she would have to learn her own hard lessons in life and suffer for her reckless selfishness.

After the long tiring climb, Gertrude was weary and soon fell asleep in the cave. She awakened when a black raven croaked to greet the dawn.

When Gertrude looked up in the blue lit cave she saw the old lady sitting at a Spinning Wheel spinning threads of her long silver hair into bright silver rings.

The old lady turned and again scolded Gertrude. "You foolish girl. You must never tell anyone of this. If you tell what you have seen you will live in disgrace. Promise me never to tell anyone, except your mother. If you promise I will give you a silver ring, and if you keep your promise only to tell your mother, the silver ring will one day turn into gold."

Gertrude promised, then pocketed the silver ring and hurried down to the village, quickly forgetting the Old Lady's warning. She wanted only to boast of her reckless risk and to display the silver ring to everyone, especially Elsa.

In the village square the villagers gathered around Gertrude. When her worried mother asked where she had been, Gertie forgot her promise and boasted how she had been in the cave and had seen the old lady spinning her silver hair into silver rings.

The villagers all laughed at Gertrude while her mother, Herr Keller and Elsa shook their heads in disbelief and dismay at Gertie the Gabbler's boasting.

Gertrude enjoyed being the centre of attention and when the villagers mocked her, Gertie gabbled more and more and exaggerated her story until the Dairyman said he did not believe her.

"I am not lying" protested Gertrude. "Look here, I have my ring in my pocket" and she put her hand in her pocket and pulled out not a ring, but a mountain berry.

Everyone laughed again at her. Gertrude felt so embarrassed and bewildered that she ran away.

Thereafter no one believed Gertrude who lived in disgrace as Gertie the Gabbler, the girl who talked too much.

When Gertrude tried to talk to Elsa at the Dairy, Elsa explained "Reden ist silber, Schweigen ist gold." meaning "Speaking is silver, silence is golden."

Not long after, Elsa married poor Wendel, the good goatherd in the village church. Everyone admired the quiet Elsa and her gold ring.

Gertrude never married and never wore a silver or a gold ring because Gertrude, the disgraced boaster, had talked too much. But Wendel always remained silent about how he got the silver ring that Elsa always wore and which had slowly turned to gold.

Gertrude always wondered if Wendel had visited the Forbidden Cave and had kept a promise to the little old lady.

How else would a poor goatherd like Wendel be able to present the modest Elsa with such a special golden wedding ring?

POOR HANS
GOLD IN THE GARDEN

POOR Hans was an unlucky peasant cowherd who lived in an old chalet high upon an alpine meadow near the mountain pass overlooking the village of Engelberg, Angel Mountain, in the remote Canton of Unterwalden. Hans always worked hard, feeding and milking his only brown cow, Lisi, or cutting hay and chopping logs. His hardworking wife Anneli also worked hard, caring for the goats, churning butter or making cheese and making bread and honeycake, while their two children, Jan and Nell fed the hens and collected mushrooms and blue berries.

In winter, when the snow lay deep, and fear of avalanches hung over the land, life was hard for the family, especially when the sly fox, who lived in the nearby fir woods, stole the chickens, or when Hans had to bring in the fire logs from the forest. The children could not go down to the village school to play with their friends and mother Anneli had no eggs for breakfast.

Often in the cold winter nights the wise old Owl sought refuge in the shelter of the hay loft and hooted his protest against the icy blizzard. Poor Hans and his family would huddle close together by the flaming log fire and throw cones on the blaze, warming their hands on mugs of Lisi's steaming milk and eating chestnuts and honeycake while telling Alpine tales.

Sometimes they had no fuel for their oil lamp, so the family would all climb up the creaky wooden stairs by candlelight and seek the comfort of their beds, huddling beneath their duvets.

On one such dark, cold wintry night large snowflakes heaped up in snowdrifts against the silent, darkened old chalet, poor Hans had a strange dream. He had a vision of the Spirit of the Mountain, the Old Man of the Alps, with his snow white beard and ice-blue eyes looking down kindly on poor Hans.

"What is troubling you Hans?" the Old Man enquired. The Cowherd was glad to tell someone of his troubles.

"Why am I so poor when I work so hard? What more can I do? I'm just not lucky! Why can't I change things?"

The Spirit of the Mountain nodded sympathetically and spoke with a voice as strong and solid as from inside the mountain itself.

"But you can change things Hans. If you want to change anything, you must also change. Change how you look at things, change how you think and act. Then you will be surprised at the changes."

Hans shook his head doubtfully. "But I'm just not lucky."

The Spirit of the Mountain sighed like a sad Alpine breeze. "Don't believe in luck," he told Hans. "Make your own luck in your own way.

Believe in yourself. You have to have a dream if you want to have a dream come true. If you don't know what you want, you won't get it. And, if you don't know where you are going, you won't get there. If you always do the same thing, you will always get the same result. Try doing something different for a change and life will change."

Poor Hans was still troubled. "All I want is not to be poor and hungry. I dream of having more cows, more goats and more chickens and food for my family."

In the morning when he awoke, he went to the cowshed and while he milked Lisi, Hans pondered how he could look at things differently and do things to change himself to change the life around him.

He could see that the garden was badly neglected, unkempt and overgrown with weeds. What a change from the garden of his grandfather who cared for it and grew beautiful flowers, vegetables and fruit bushes that long ago had fed the whole family.

Hans shook his head in shame and remembered how it had all been so different, so fruitful and nourishing to feed the whole of Grandfather's family when Hans was only a boy.

"I wish I could change it back - I wish I could make it a garden again but I'm not a gardener and I'm different from Grandfather."

Then he remembered the words of the Old Man of the Alps - "If you want to change something you must first change yourself."

Hans decided he needed to change the garden so, for a change he went to the garden shed and took out an old rusty spade. "I'll try to be a gardener for a change" he said and started digging up the weeds and turning the soil. To his surprise he enjoyed himself - "It's a change from chopping logs", he muttered to himself as he dug deeper and deeper into the soil - even deeper than Grandfather ever dug.

Suddenly the spade struck a hard stone - it would not go deeper. As Hans bent down to take out the stone something glinted in the sun. "That's not a stone. Stones don't shine like this", he said to himself, as he hurriedly scraped away the soil. There in the sunshine glinted a bright coin, and another, yet another and another.

"Gold, gold, gold," he shouted as he excitedly tossed the coins in the air like confetti.

Anneli stopped churning the milk in the butter churn and ran out of the chalet with Jan and Nell. They all ran about picking up gold pieces that Hans was throwing about with excitement. Then they all gathered around the hole in the earth and marvelled at the hoard of Roman gold coins that a Roman Centurion had buried on the mountain Pass when he was attacked by the men of the mountain centuries ago.

"What good luck," shouted Anneli, but Hans merely replied "Not luck but doing something different. Not the usual chopping wood but the unusual gardening!"

And he echoed the words of the Spirit of the Mountain, "If you want things to change, you first have to change yourself. You have to have a dream if you want a dream to come true."

And so the next day Hans, Anneli and the children put all the gold coins in their rucksacks and happily marched down to the Village Market place. Hans bought another cow and a new spade. Anneli bought another goat and oil for the lamps while the children bought more hens and bedtime story books.

And still there were coins left. So Hans shared the rest of his good fortune with the villagers. The village Elders thanked Hans and said "You deserve the Good Luck and Good Fortune for all your hard work, Hans."

The cowherd looked up at the Mountain and remembered the words of the Old Man of the Alps - "We make our own luck. We may stand on our own Good Fortune and not see it because we look at things the same way. To change things we must change ourselves."

And that is how life changed for the poor cowherd when he changed how he looked at things.

THE DARK LAKE
THE MYSTERY OF DUNKELSEE

ONE morning after breakfast muesli, Grandma told the family she did not want to cook the usual dinner that night. Instead of the usual cheese Fondue, the roast potato Rösti or omelette, she wanted nice fresh fish.

So Grandpa took his old fishing rod down to the lake stream along with Jan, who wanted to learn to catch fish.

At the lake Grandpa told Jan how glad he was that they lived by the bright, sparkling Lake Luzern, the Vierwaldstattersee, The Lake of the Four Woods, and not by the gloomy, murky Dark Lake, the Dunkelsee, which had no fish in the deep, black waters.

Jan was puzzled. How could Switzerland, his beautiful homeland of clear, clean mirror-bright waters have one dark, sunless lake?

While Grandpa sat watching his fishing line in Lake Luzern's crystal waters he told Jan the story of the fishless, Dark Lake.

* * *

LONG ago there was a prosperous farmer in a beautiful sunny valley. The Farmer, Herr Bodmer was a good living, hardworking man and his wife Frau Bodmer was also respected as a generous, pious lady, who was kindly to the poor and elderly mountain folk and villagers.

The Bodmer couple lived according to their ancestral family Motto carved on the portal of their solid stone Farmhouse - "Fromm,

49

Freigebig, Fröhlich, Frei", meaning "Righteous, Generous, Cheerful, Free." And accordingly Herr and Frau Bodmer were liked, respected, honoured and renowned by all their neighbours and the mountain Berglers of the region.

The couple had two daughters, Bertha and Martha, who were completely different from their parents. These two sisters shamed the good Bodmer name by their wicked, selfish, miserable and narrow minded attitude and conduct, unlike their Mother and Father and contrary to their hereditary family Motto. Neither sister was liked or respected by anyone who knew them.

Because both Bertha and Martha lacked the qualities of their parents it grieved their kind hearted mother, who slowly and painfully died of anguish, and a heavy heart. The sisters also grieved their aging father, who was too old and infirm to discipline and change the behaviour of his wayward and arrogant daughters.

As Father Bodmer grew more ashamed of his two daughters he became more generous to the mountain folk and villagers. He took greater pride in his prosperous farm, especially his apple and cherry orchards, as well as his golden cornfields at harvest time.

But he never stored more grain in his granary than he, his family and farm workers needed to feed themselves. The remainder he gave to the poor folk who were also invited to pick the apples and cherries.

His daughters expected to inherit their rich father's wealth and competed in wasting their Mother's money buying silly town dresses and shoes and gaudy jewellery to be better than each other. The more money they wasted on themselves in the city, the more ridiculous they appeared to the country folk, who laughed at them.

When Farmer Bodmer died in distress at his selfish daughters' behaviour there was great mourning for the loss of this good man in the region.

The only two persons who did not lament or were sorrowful at his passing were the grasping sisters, who secretly gloated over their inheritance of the richly flourishing estate.

When the next harvest came the local folk arrived at the farm to gather grain, apples and cherries for the sisters and for themselves as they had in all the many years before Farmer Bodmer died. But to the villagers' astonishment the ill mannered sisters ordered their farm workers to drive away the poor local folk without any grain or fruit. Instead all the corn and fruit was harvested and all sold by the greedy sisters in the village market.

As Bertha and Martha counted all the money from the Market, they began to quarrel angrily over their shares. Their argument became so bitter with so many angry words, accusing each other of cheating and how to divide the money, that the only thing they could agree about was to divide the whole of the Father's estate. After much haggling they bargained to halve the fields and halve the ancestral home itself with one sister living on the ground floor and the other sister to live on the top floor.

They each argued that since they could not live kindly together, they should separate and live selfishly apart.

After that the quarrelsome sisters became even more quarrelsome with each other and more disagreeable to their neighbours and villagers. Matters worsened as their quarrel went from bad to worse. So they finally decided the only thing they could do was to direct the local Auctioneer to sell the whole Bodmer estate, and with their profits, go their separate ways far from each other.

On the day for the Auction Sale no one arrived there to buy the property, nor did the Auctioneer. No one could arrive, no one could reach the Farm because it had been raining so heavily in the night, that the flood waters had washed away the farm road and the bridge over the stream to the property. Above it all the black clouds still deluged the estate with dark rainwater. Only the two quarrelsome sisters' dislike and enmity for each other was blacker than the black thunder clouds. All the time Bertha and Martha remained in the separate accommodations with their separate unhappy lives, brooding and scheming ways to hurt each other and unaware that outside the rainstorm was flooding their property. If they had known it might have drowned their dislike for each other.

When the rainstorm did at long last stop, the Auctioneer and the local folk left the village to go down to the Farm Sale. As they neared the valley, all they could see was a great lake that had flooded, and submerged the whole farm, land and orchards. Even the ancestral Farm House had vanished under the dark waters and nowhere were the two sisters to be seen.

All had vanished under the thunderstorm when the river dam at the top of the valley had been burst by the raging flood waters that drowned everything and the two spiteful and quarrelsome sisters with their destructive squabble.

Today the waters of the Dark Lake are as gloomy and murky as the quarrelsome sisters' quarrels and there are no fish or living creatures in the Dark Lake as it was poisoned by the sisters' hatred.

* * *

As Grandpa finished his story and taught Jan to catch the silver trout and perch in the crystal, bright waters of Lake Luzern, he said "And now you know why no one ever tries to catch fish in the dead, dull water of the Dark Lake, Dunkelsee."

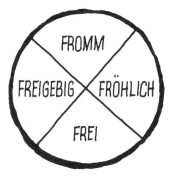

LUKAS AND THE EVERLASTING CHEESE

NOT all Mountain Spirits and Alpine Imps are mischievous or malicious. Some are kind and benevolent and one of the kindest is The Guardian of the Pastures, The Green Guardian. He guards the cows, the goats and the herdsmen and milkmaids from the winter snow storms, avalanches and fir forest fires.

But while He protects the alpine animals and farm folk his Word is law and he must be obeyed. Wise mountaineers and herdsmen know this even when times are difficult on the snow covered peaks.

Often the herdsmen are on the high alps for many days tending their cattle or rescuing goats that have slipped on the ice into a crevasse or snowdrift. So frequently the young men or milkmaids go hungry and have only cows milk to drink.

Early one morning when the mountain mist clouded the alpine pasture a young calf slipped on the wet grass and tumbled headlong down into the rocky gorge.

Lukas, the young Cowherd bravely clambered down the steep ravine to rescue the terrified calf. He carried the animal over his shoulders and slowly scrambled back up the rocky slope to the pasture and the calf's welcoming mother cow.

Young Lukas collapsed on the wet grass, exhausted and hungry, waiting to feel strong enough to lead his herd back to a safer place.

As he lay there dreaming of a big meal of rye bread with cheese and red grapes, the shadow of the Green Guardian of the Pastures fell across him. "Well done, Lukas. You saved the calf. What were you dreaming about?"

Lukas wearily explained he was exhausted and hungry and all he wanted was a good meal of bread and cheese.

The Green Guardian opened his knapsack and produced a wheel of alpine cheese and commanded "Take it Lukas and enjoy it. You deserve a reward.but never eat all of it - always leave a little morsel for the next day."

Lukas was overjoyed and grasped the gift. "But, but ..." he mumbled "My Grandmother and Mother always told me to eat all my meal and not to leave anything on the plate."

The Green Guardian nodded agreement. "Your Grandmother and Mother are wise not to waste their good food. But this cheese is different, it's a reward for courage."

Lukas took a big bite of the cheese and while he was munching away at it the Green Guardian commanded "Do as I tell you. This cheese has the magical quality that when it is eaten it will grow back to its original size between meals - as long as it is not all eaten so something is left. You must leave a small piece for the next meal - otherwise the whole cheese will disappear."

The Green Guardian's command was quite clear. "Don't be greedy, don't eat it all at once," before the Guardian waved farewell and strode away up to the snow covered peak.

Thereafter each day Lukas enjoyed his hearty cheese meal.

Although Lukas was fearless he was also forgetful sometimes and the next week when he was hungry again after leading the herd around the highest pastures he could not resist the mysterious alpine cheese. The temptation was too great and he hungrily devoured the whole cheese.

Then as he gobbled the last morsel, he suddenly remembered the Green Guardian's command "Do not eat it all."

Lukas nearly choked - but it was too late, not a piece, not a crumb remained.

And because not a morsel remained, there was no more magical cheese to grow again. The next day and the next day when Lukas was hungry, there was no cheese left to eat.

So often Lukas and the Cowherds had to return with the herds on the long cattle drives down to their homes in the valley to milk the cows and make their own cheese. And they never saw the Green Guardian of the Pastures again. He is waiting to reward the next hero of the Alps.

GRANDMA LILLY'S OWN CHRISTMAS STORY

AS Christmas was soon coming the snow was falling deeply over the mountainside. Grandma reminded Grandpa to go to the forest for a Christmas tree for the family to decorate for their Yuletide festivities.

Each Christmas the family all gathered around the big log fire in their old chalet for their special Christmas feast of chicken, pies and sweetmeats and to exchange their home-made gifts.

While Grandma busily prepared for the delicious dinner on Christmas day, Grandpa took his axe from the woodshed and went up to the forest for the Christmas tree. When he returned covered in snow, and looking like a snowman with the snow covered tree, Grandma wouldn't let him into her nice clean house with all that snow. She reminded him that he must finish chopping up the wood pile for the log fire to cook the dinner and roast the chestnuts.

So poor old Grandpa went back into the cold woodshed and chopped up the fire logs until darkness fell. When Grandpa did come back into the cosy chalet, Grandma gently sat him down in his comfy fireside chair with his own big mug of warm milk and thick slice of honey cake.

Soon he nodded off to sleep - before telling the family his usual bedtime folk tales, his alpine legends and his fireside fables.

Everyone was disappointed, but Grandma was firm. Grandpa was not to be disturbed. Although Grandpa was the Master of his farm, Grandma was the Mistress of the Chalet, and her word was Law in the household. So Grandpa went on gently snoring because Grandma's command was obeyed. And the family fell silent until little Ellen Sarah said quietly "Grandma, will you tell us a Christmas story, please?"

Grandma glanced at the sleeping Grandpa and rather than awaken the old man, Grandma agreed and gathered the family around her.

She remembered the time long ago as a young woman, when she was a school teacher in the town of Bern and how her pupils enjoyed her tales, especially her up to date stories like this one.

Grandma Lilly's own Christmas tale.

* * *

How Jan got a Special Red Candle from Switzerland.

LONG ago when Grandma was a girl, one year near Christmas time, Santa Claus was busy in his mountain Grotto preparing for his long sleigh-ride down the valley to the village of Flamatt in Canton Fribourg to deliver his Christmas gifts to the children of the Hesterberg Hamlet.

He loaded his sleigh with all the sacks and bags he had filled with nuts, chocolates, apples and almond cakes for the deserving Hesterberg Hamlet children. He also put in a sour lemon for the village boy who threw snowballs at girls.

In the night time it had been snowing and the fir trees were laden with fresh snowflakes that almost covered up the forest track down to the valley. Santa's little dog, Waldi, who always trotted in front of the sleigh, tried to run faster to warm up his cold nose and cold paws. And Santa's brave little helper, Zack the Dwarf, had to hop, skip and jump over the snow to keep up with Waldi and Santa's sleigh.

When Santa, Waldi and Zack arrived at Flamatt, they went immediately to Hesterberg Hamlet. There the children were building a giant snowman. Rolfi and Ursuli Hesterberg, Maimi and the twins, Brigitti and Barbeli Moser, as well as Thomas and Marcus Schlumpf - all the Hamlet children were there except one - the boy called Jan Murray.

When Santa asked for Jan, his best friend Ursuli explained they hadn't seen Jan that day and perhaps he had gone to Bern to see the town's famous bears in Bern's Bear Pit.

As Santa and Zack placed the bags of gifts under the Hesterberg Christmas tree, Santa mumbled "I must find Jan, because I have a present for him as well."

But Santa had other children's' gifts to deliver in Flamatt, so he sent his assistant Zack, the Dwarf, to the Bear Pit in Bern. Zack ran as fast as his little legs could carry him and because he was wearing his special dwarf's snowshoes, he soon arrived at the Bear Pit. The five bears were outside their dens and were tumbling and rolling about in the snow, wrestling each other for a carrot.

They only stopped their jostling and tumbling when Zack called to them "Hallo Bears, have you seen Jan Murray of Flamatt? You know, that little boy who came from Scotland."

Brownie, the biggest bear, replied "Of course we know him. That Scottish laddie wears a kilt even on the coldest days." Zack was pleased.

"That's right Brownie. Jan came to Switzerland with his Papa and Mama. Where is he now?" Brownie shook his head, saying "Sorry Zack, we haven't seen him today."

Dwarf Zack felt miserable and told the three bears he must find Jan for his Master, Santa. Then Blackie, the middle bear, said he would climb up the tree in the Bear Pit to see if he could see Jan. But when he climbed down again, he shook his head, and told Zack there was no sign of the Scots lad.

Ginger, the smallest bear, advised Zack to go to the Giant's Castle to meet the Giant who is so tall he can see over the tops of houses, the forests and mountains.

So off Zack ran again as far as his little legs could carry him to the Giant's Castle.

When he arrived there the castle Drawbridge was pulled up which meant the Giant was not at home. Poor little Zack was out of luck again and big tears began rolling down the Dwarf's cheeks as he sobbed "What can I do now?" A squeaky voice behind him said "Don't despair, Zack. Go to the Fairy Lady for help." It was the red Squirrel speaking from the fir tree. "Come along Zack" said the Squirrel "I'll show you where the Fairy Lady lives" and with that the Squirrel hopped from tree to tree. Little Zack puffed breathlessly, as he followed the Squirrel until they finally arrived at the Fairy Lady's cottage.

While Zack was standing outside, a deep stern voice commanded "You, little man! What do you want here?" It was the Drummer Boy, her Ladyship's bodyguard. Zack explained his task. And after the Drummer Boy heard that Santa was seeking Jan, he opened the garden gate and told Zack to follow the Melon Maiden, the Fairy Lady's handmaiden into the cottage. Inside the Lady welcomed Zack and said she would help him. So she gave him a slice of chocolate cake because he looked hungry, and while he was eating the Lady spread out a large map on the cottage stone floor, saying "Look, Zack, do you see that land way up in the North towards the North Pole and in the cold North Sea? Well, that's Scotland. That's where Jan went home with his Mama and Papa, back to the Highlands after their stay in the Alps and the Hesterberg Hamlet. They had to leave early in the morning before they could say goodbye to the villagers."

Zack stared at the map with its northern land of the Scots, Scotland. "It's so far away across the sea. I'll never reach Jan" and before he could burst into tears the Fairy Lady patted his head and replied "Don't despair, Zack. Take this Old Shoe full of pennies I've earned from my hard work helping people. Give it all to Santa, and ask Santa to buy a big Red Christmas candle and send it to Jan to brighten the Scottish laddie's Christmas Day in the cold, dark, misty north land."

So, Zack hurried with the Shoe of pennies back to Santa, who had just finished his delivery rounds of gifts and had only one present left -- the gift he had brought for Jan was a pair of new skis.

After hearing the Fairy Lady's request for a Red Candle to brighten Jan's Christmas in misty Scotland, Santa took the new skis to another special little boy, Hansli, who helped the old ladies of the village carry their shopping baskets.

Then Santa and Zack went to Herr Egli's village shop and with all the Shoe pennies bought a big beautiful thick Red Christmas Candle and wrapped it up with colourful Christmas paper.

As it was getting dark, Santa, Zack and Waldi all hurried back over the deepening snow up the mountain to the Ice Palace of the Yuletide Angel at Engelberg, the Angel Mountain.

The Yule Angel agreed to fly with the Red Candle over the Seas to Jan before it got too dark to find his way to the far north.

That's why on every Christmas Eve at sunset the Yule Angel travels on a small golden cloud over the mountains, the plains, the valleys and the seas carrying the Candle from the Alps to the Highlands for Jan's Christmas morning surprise.

And each Christmas when Jan lights the thick Red Candle he knows that Santa Claus, Zack the Dwarf, little Waldi and the children of Hesterberg Hamlet and especially the Fairy Lady of Bern have remembered him and hope he will return to Switzerland.

* * *

When Grandma Lilly finished telling her own Christmas Story the children who were gathered around her excitedly shouted "Please Grandma, tell us your Christmas Story again."

All their shouts awakened Grandpa Mark who said "Next year I shall tell you my Christmas Story."